ENGLISH
for the more able

Mary Green

Contents

Introduction 3

Term 1

Spelling strategies 4

Pick and choose 5

Language changes..6

Snug's roar 7

Writing sentences to create effects......................8

On the lookout 9

The author's craft 10

Roland 11

Modern retellings 12

Telling tales 13

Different perspectives 14

Points of view 15

Playscripts 16

Things on my mind 17

Using kennings to personify 18

A kenning 19

Autobiography...20

Elocution contests..21

Editorials..22

Newspaper report..23

Term 2

Inventing mnemonics 24

Mnemonics...25

Proverbs...26

Proverb poem 27

Active and passive 28

Agent Bradshaw's log...................................29

Using conditionals 30

Problem page..31

Conveying the passing of time 32

Time passing..33

Playing with meaning 34

A poem from 0 to 10.....................................35

Stock characters 36

Iago...37

Parody..38

Hiawatha 39

Writing an argument 40

A tricky question...41

Writing a balanced report 42

Child stars...43

Term 3

Extending vocabulary....................................44

Don't use big words 45

Creating word games 46

One at a time...47

Creating jokes 48

Have you heard the one about ...? 49

Plans and directions......................................50

This way or that?...51

Regional speech...52

A Very Honorable Guy 53

Linked images 54

A poem of images 55

Comparing and contrasting 56

Comparing two poems...................................57

Reviews..58

A book review..59

Skimming and scanning 60

Egges in Mustarde or Tarte of Cheese? 61

Selecting the style...62

Helping Kitty 63

Objectives grid 64

Introduction

The series *English for the More Able*, books 1–6, has been written for primary school children whose performance is above their chronological age and who need particularly challenging tasks. It is assumed they will have wide reading experience, a good command of language, have acquired problem-solving skills and can work independently. Intervention by the teacher can therefore be minimal.

Book 6 in the series is targeted at children aged 10–11years. The tasks included in each activity sheet relate to the objectives in the *National Literacy Strategy*, drawing on word, sentence and text levels, and are divided into three terms. However, the activity sheets do not have to be followed in chronological order. You may wish to use them at alternative times throughout the year, according to your needs.

The material and language tasks selected cover a wide range of subjects, genres and writing styles. For example, 'Snug's roar' in Term 1 takes as its focus an extract from Shakespeare's *A Midsummer Night's Dream* and the use of archaic language, while 'Have you heard the one about … ?' in Term 3 looks at the language of jokes, which are often told in the present tense to create a sense of immediacy.

The teacher page
Each activity sheet is accompanied by a page of supporting notes giving advice and information about how to use the activities. It is organised under the following sub-headings.

● **Learning objectives**
The skills on which each activity sheet is based are outlined here.

● **Activity sheet/Expectations**
This describes the content of the activity sheet, and elaborates on the objectives above. It also gives the teacher an indication of the kinds of skills required by the children and what to expect from them. Examples are often given and, where appropriate, specific answers.

● **Further activities**
Suggestions are offered on how to develop further the skills and tasks detailed in the activity sheets. These may involve extended work (such as creating a booklet over time), research work (such as using ICT) or shorter tasks.

● **Resources**
This lists the relevant activity sheet, together with information on useful equipment and books, such as poems, reference and other non-fiction texts.

Objectives grid
This appears on page 64, and it provides a quick, easy-to-consult guide to the skills covered in the activity sheets.

Spelling strategies

Learning objectives

Word level
- *To use independent spelling strategies.*

Text level
- *To comment critically on the language, style, success of examples of non-fiction such as leaflets.*
- To create a spelling advice leaflet for other children to use.

Activity sheet/Expectations

The main activity outlined here, creating a spelling advice leaflet, is suitable for those children who are independent and able spellers. Not only will the final leaflet be a useful resource for other children, but it will also help able spellers to identify a range of useful strategies for recalling their own troublesome spellings. The activity sheet prepares the ground by presenting the children with a range of spellings and suggesting possible ways in which these can be recalled. The children need to match the spelling with a useful strategy or strategies. They should use their own judgement and be able to justify their choices. The following suggestions are given:

precipitation: A, F, H and I (*pre-* and *-tion*);

daughter: B (for example *caught*);

Egypt: E;

receive: C ('*i* before *e* except after *c*');

inventiveness: D, G (such as *invent*), I (*-ive* and *-ness*).

Further activities

Once the activity sheet has been completed, ask pairs to agree the best strategies for recalling particular kinds of words and to think of examples. Prompt the children to add any further general advice that might go in the leaflet, for example: *Identify spellings you often get wrong and record them in a spelling book; Make a list of common words that are often misspelled.*

The children can then create their own individual spelling advice leaflets, choosing their own spelling tips. If possible, they should use ICT design tools. For example, they could use borders and a range of fonts in different colours, and also drawing tools. Encourage a high standard of presentation. Also prompt the children to consider how to sequence the information, for example they might like to use one page for each kind of strategy.

Have available, and ask the children to collect, a range of leaflets that can be compared for clarity, language and style, and also for layout and presentation, for example public health leaflets and those detailing local events. The children can use the best of these as models for their own spelling advice leaflets.

Resources

AS 'Pick and choose'; a range of leaflets; computer for ICT work

Pick and choose

Name: .... **Date:** ....

1. Study the spellings below and the tips for remembering them. Match the tips to the spellings by writing down the letters. More than one tip may be useful for each spelling!

Spellings	Useful tips
precipitation	....
daughter	....
Egypt	....
receive	....
inventiveness	....

Tips	
A.	Splitting words into syllables
B.	Thinking of words from the same word family or with the same letter string
C.	Using spelling rules or conventions
D.	Building from words you know
E.	Using the shape of words
F.	Using mnemonics for the part of the word you forget
G.	Using the meaning of words
H.	Using prefixes

2. Do you know the 'Look, Cover, Write, Check' (LCWC) method of learning spellings? How might it help you with your spelling? Why do you think some people add 'Say' to 'Look, Cover, Write, Check' (LSCWC)?

3. Write some words of your own and the tips you use to remember the spellings.

4. Make your own spelling leaflet, full of tips and examples for other children to use:

● Select some useful spelling methods and examples. (You don't have to include them all.)

● Plan the presentation of your leaflet. Think about the cover, the title, whether you will have an introduction or not, and page numbering.

● Choose a user-friendly style of presentation, and lay out your advice clearly.

Can you think of anything else?

Language changes

Learning objectives

Word level

● *To understand how words and expressions have changed over time, for example old verb endings -st and -th and how some words have fallen out of use.*

Activity Sheet/Expectations

The extract on the activity sheet is taken from *A Midsummer Night's Dream*, Act III Scene I. The mechanicals are discussing the play they are to perform at Duke Theseus' wedding. Snug is to play the lion, but the audience must not be afraid of the lion and Bottom offers his suggestions for how to play the role.

Though much of the vocabulary and language style is archaic, it is intelligible and children who are confident and fluent readers should be able to understand the text. It is useful, however, if pairs are given the opportunity to read aloud or act out the speech.

A

Archaic terms:

Nay = No, *thus* = this, *defect* = effect, *entreat you* = plead, *hither* = here, *pity of my life* = take pity, *I am much afeared* = I am afraid, *Think on'st* = think about it, *It shall be so* = it'll be done, *Why, you must not* = don't, *Say'st thou* = Do you say, *Whether thou wilt or no* = whether or not you will, *Thou art* = you are, *Ay, it doth* = Yes, it does, *is't not enough* = it isn't enough, *Goeth thus* = go on, *Thou art a rogue* = you are a rascal, *Couldst we* = could we, *Go thither* = go there, *Wouldst she* = would she, *How now* = what's going on.

Pairs can also discuss their own scripts, or you may prefer them to work together on a single dialogue. When the children have completed the modern dialogue, they should rewrite it using archaic language. Phrases are provided to support them but, to create a convincing dialogue, children will also need to capture the cadence of the sentences. It would therefore be useful to offer them opportunities to read the whole scene from the play, noting the interactions between the players.

The children need to grasp that although vocabulary (such as slang) can change rapidly, the meaning of language is still accessible, over time.

Note: You might like to have some dictionaries available that include definitions of archaic language. *Shakespeare's Stories* by Leon Garfield is a modern retelling of a selection of Shakespeare's plays, including *A Midsummer Night's Dream*. It is beautifully written and is useful to have available along with the original plays.

Further activities

The children could act out the two versions of their dialogues for other members of the class and modify these in the light of their performances.

Resources

AS 'Snug's roar'; dictionaries; *Shakespeare's Stories* by Leon Garfield (Penguin Books)

Snug's roar

Name: .... **Date:** ....

1. Read the following extract from Act III Scene I of *A Midsummer Night s Dream* by William Shakespeare. A group of workmen are discussing how to perform their play for Duke Theseus. Bottom is explaining the way Snug should play the lion.

> **Bottom:** Nay, you must name his name, and half his face must be seen through the lion's neck; and he himself must speak through, saying thus, or to the same defect, 'Ladies', or, 'fair ladies, I would wish you', or, 'I would request you', or, 'I would entreat you, not to fear, not to tremble: my life for yours. If you think I come hither as a lion, it were pity of my life: no, I am no such thing; I am a man as other men are': and there, indeed, let him name his name, and tell them plainly he is Snug the joiner.

2. How does Bottom think the lion should be played? Give a reason for your answer.

3. Underline all the words and phrases in the extract that we do not use today, and work out what they mean.

4. Write a short modern dialogue between two children. Focus on a problem, for example they are late for school, or one has lost their bag or swapped something valuable for something not worth having. Whatever the situation, they are plotting an excuse to tell their teacher or parents.

5. Now rewrite your dialogue using archaic language. You can change it and introduce new events if you wish, such as a quarrel, but it should sound convincing. Use some of the words and phrases below and any from Bottom's speech, along with any others you know.

I am much afeared	Think on'st	It shall be so	Why, you must not	Say'st thou
Whether thou wilt or no	Thou art	Ay, it doth	Is't not enough	Goeth thus
Thou art a rogue	Couldst we	Go thither	Wouldst she	How, now

Writing sentences to create effects

Learning objectives

Sentence level
- *To form complex sentences through using different connecting devices; exploring how meaning is affected by the sequence of clauses.*
- *To secure knowledge and understanding of more sophisticated punctuation marks: the semicolon and to use this in their own writing.*

Text level
- *To be familiar with the work of some established authors, and to know what is special about their work.*

Activity Sheet/Expectations

The short extract on the activity sheet is taken from Charles Dickens' *Our Mutual Friend* at the beginning of Chapter 1, 'On the lookout'. It describes Jesse Hexam or 'Gaffer' Hexam, whose sinister occupation is to look for corpses in the River Thames (though this is not declared here). A mystery is created through the description.

The extract has been chosen because it allows the children to look closely at the way in which Dickens has structured the sentence and how this creates particular effects. There are particular features that reoccur in Dickens' writing, some of which are present here, for instance: the use of repetition; the use of semicolons which extend sentences and build a scene. (Semicolons are used less often in contemporary fiction.) The children are encouraged to identify semicolons together with the use of the conditional *could*. In particular, they should notice how the scene is presented by using the negatives, *no* and *not*, so that the scene is built up through what is not there, rather than what is. This effect is then undercut in the final clause when speculation is replaced by certainty: *but he looked for something, with a most intent and searching gaze* to create impact.

Allow the children to read and reread the extract with expression (and preferably aloud) to help them appreciate how well-paced it is.

Further activities

Ask the children to extend their descriptions. They should combine their sentence with a series of further short and long sentences, which will add variation and create a longer paragraph.

Children can also study the way in which Dickens uses hyperbole, in particular to create comic characters and scenes (for examples, see 'The Pickwickians' in the *Pickwick Papers*).

In addition, many of Dickens' story openings are powerful and use the techniques discussed above (for examples, see *Little Dorrit* and *Bleak House*), offering a great opportunity to explore more complex sentences further.

Resources

AS 'On the lookout'; other Dickens' books, such as *Little Dorrit, A Tale of Two Cities, Pickwick Papers* and *Bleak House*

On the lookout

Name: .... **Date:** ....

1. Read the extract below, which is taken from *Our Mutual Friend* by Charles Dickens. The novel was published in 1865 and the story is set during the Victorian period.

The Scene

It is an autumn evening. A boat of *dirty and disreputable appearance* can be seen on the River Thames between Southwark Bridge and London Bridge. There are two figures in the boat, a man and his daughter.

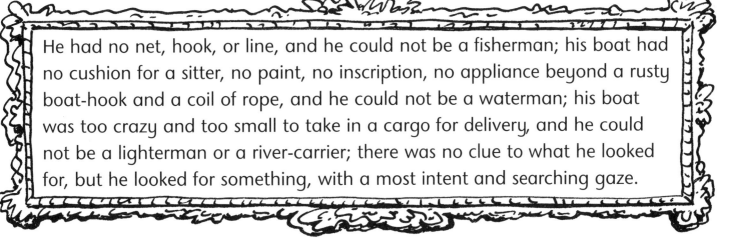

He had no net, hook, or line, and he could not be a fisherman; his boat had no cushion for a sitter, no paint, no inscription, no appliance beyond a rusty boat-hook and a coil of rope, and he could not be a waterman; his boat was too crazy and too small to take in a cargo for delivery, and he could not be a lighterman or a river-carrier; there was no clue to what he looked for, but he looked for something, with a most intent and searching gaze.

2. What do you think the man could be looking for on the river?

3. Read the extract again and underline all the words that make a negative, such as *no* and *not*, and also all the conditionals such as *could*. Can you see how they are repeated?

4. In what way is the last clause, *but he looked for something, with a most intent and searching gaze*, different from the other clauses?

5. The extract is one long sentence made up of other sentences and clauses. What punctuation joins them?

6. Now write your own long sentence using the extract as a model.
Choose from the following situations or think of your own:
● someone in a disused lighthouse
● someone circling low in a small plane
● someone climbing on to a roof without any equipment
● someone walking in torrential rain without a coat.

You do not have to use as many commas as Dickens, but join small sentences and clauses with punctuation, such as semicolons, dashes or brackets.
Give your description an unusual title.

The author's craft

Learning objectives

Text level
- *To articulate personal responses to literature, identifying why and how a text affects a reader.*
- *To manipulate narrative perspective by writing in the voice and style of a text.*

Activity Sheet/Expectations

The extract on the activity sheet is taken from Alan Garner's classic fantasy novel *Elidor*. One of the text's most interesting characteristics is the way in which the pace of the writing and the events mirror the note played on the fiddle.

The activity asks the children to identify the effect the writing has on the reader and how this is achieved. Initially, it would be useful if they worked in pairs to discuss the extract, sharing their individual responses and deciding what the blind fiddler represents and what the outcomes for the different characters might be.

Then, individually, the children should look at how the story is crafted. They are asked on the activity sheet to identify particular techniques, the purpose of which is to gain some understanding of:
- how the author maintains the reader's attention, for example by creating and maintaining a sense of mystery;
- how the different effects are created through description and dialogue. (The detailed description contrasts with the short, sharp dialogue);
- how the pace of the writing alters and the way tension is built up;
- how surprise is created, for example the description of the fiddler playing is juxtaposed with sharp dialogue.

The children's own descriptions can be worked on and redrafted to form the basis of a story. The children can also introduce further perspectives into their stories by presenting events through the eyes of more than one narrator or character.

Further activities

If possible, show the children the beginning of *Elidor* and draw their attention to the quotation *Childe Roland to the dark tower came*. Point out that it comes from Edgar's speech in *King Lear*. It is also the title of a poem by Robert Browning. Ask the children to find the connection between *Elidor*, Robert Browning and a play by William Shakespeare. Prompt the children to carry out research by studying *Elidor*, using the library and ICT and asking others. It is also useful if the children are introduced to the notion that authors draw on earlier literature for their ideas.

Resources

AS 'Roland'; *Elidor* by Alan Garner (Collins); *The School Bag* edited by Seamus Heaney and Ted Hughes (Faber); library books; computer for Internet research

Roland

Name: .... **Date:** ....

1. Read the following extract from *Elidor* by Alan Garner.

Nick, Helen, David and Roland pass through streets of empty houses until they come to a church that is being demolished. They see an old blind man standing alone playing a violin. Strange things begin to happen. Roland goes into the church where he sees the blind fiddler.

Roland went down the stairs, a step at a time, dazed but no longer frightened. The church was somehow remote from him now, and flat, like a piece of stage scenery. The only real things were the fiddler and his bow.

"I heard your music," said Roland. "Why were you playing so far away from people?"

"I was near you. Are you not people?" They had reached the bottom of the stairs, and were standing on the earth floor of the church. "Give me my bow."

"I can't stay," said Roland. But the old man put the fiddle to his shoulder. "I'm looking for my sister, and my two brothers –" The old man began to play. "– and I must find them before dark –" It was the wild dance. "– and we've a train to catch. What's that noise? – Please! – Stop! – It's hurting! – Please! –"

The air took up the fiddler's note. It was the sound Roland had heard upstairs, but now it was louder, building waves that jarred the church, and went through Roland's body until he felt that he was threaded on the sound.

"– Please! –"

"Now! Open the door!"

"I can't! It's locked!"

"Open it! There is little time!"

"But – !"

"Now!"

Roland stumbled to the door, grasped the iron handle, and pulled with all his weight. The door opened, and he ran out on to the cobbles of the street, head down, driven by the noise.

But he never reached the far pavement, for the cobbles were moving under him. He turned. The outline of the church rippled in the air, and vanished. He was standing among boulders on a sea shore, and the music died into the crash of breakers, and the long fall of surf.

2. How does the writer make you want to read on? Underline the parts of the extract that give you clues. Think about the use of powerful verbs, punctuation, the change of speed between the paragraphs, the difference between the characters and the effect the ending has.

3. Write your own description about strange events in the same style as the extract. Change the setting in your description.

Modern retellings

Learning objectives

Text level
- *To manipulate narrative perspective by: writing in the voice and style of a text; producing a modern retelling.*

Activity Sheet/Expectations

Historically, most well-known fairy tales have been rewritten or changed in the telling. Sometimes they have been deliberately altered to fit into the prevailing values of the time. One of the most well-documented examples of this is the rewriting of fairy tales by the Brothers Grimm.

The activity sheet asks the children to combine two tales into one and to alter the plots and character traits. This task is more challenging than rewriting one tale only and encourages greater inventiveness. The children are also asked to retain the fairy tale style and to include minor characters, though these too should have different character traits if appropriate.

The star charts on the activity sheet provide examples that the children can use as models to plan their own fairy tales. The children should select their own stories and then write down possible changes to the characters and plot. The emphasis should be on challenging assumptions.

Children with different cultural experiences may wish to draw on other fairy or folk tales (though it is interesting that the same stories, such as 'Cinderella', sometimes known as 'Sapsorrow', and 'Sleeping Beauty' occur in slightly different forms across several cultures).

Further activities

The children can experiment by changing the endings of several well-known folk and fairy tales. These can provide interesting material for group discussion, in which the children look at the effects these endings have on the different characters.

Ask the children to carry out research into picture books for small children, identifying those in which the child or animal character has some control over the action and those which question particular assumptions. For example, *Best Friends For Frances* by Russell and Lilian Hoban, the *Horrid Henry* series by Francesca Simon and *Black Angels* by Rita Murphy, all for older readers, challenge assumptions or break rules. *The Forest Princess* by Harriet Herman Berkeley is a retelling of 'Rapunzel'.

Resources

AS 'Telling tales'; *Best Friends For Frances* by Russell and Lilian Hoban (Picture Puffin); the *Horrid Henry* series by Francesca Simon (Orion); *Black Angels* by Rita Murphy (Bantam Doubleday Dell); *The Forest Princess* by Harriet Herman (Rainbow Press)

Telling tales

Name: .... **Date:** ....

You are going to create a new fairy tale by taking two you already know and combining them. Change the plots and change what the characters are like. Look at the star charts below first to help you.

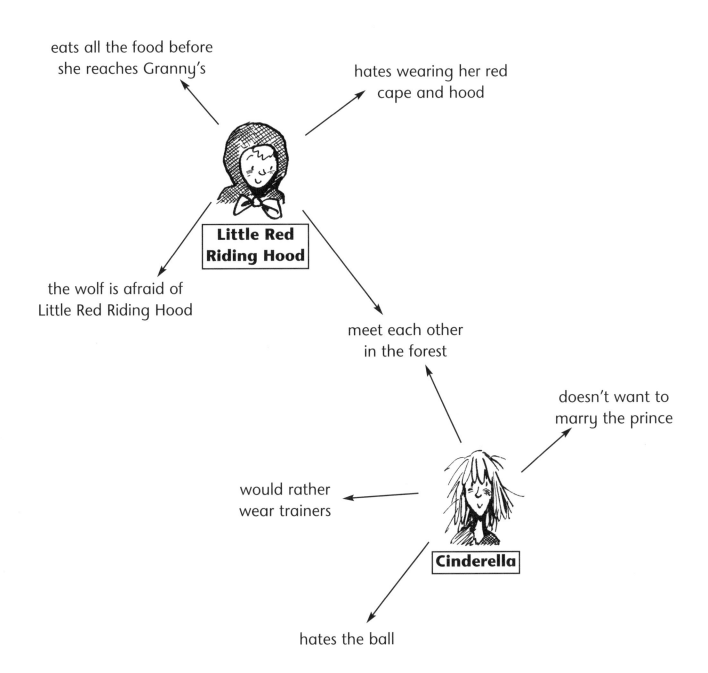

eats all the food before
she reaches Granny's

hates wearing her red
cape and hood

**Little Red
Riding Hood**

the wolf is afraid of
Little Red Riding Hood

meet each other
in the forest

doesn't want to
marry the prince

would rather
wear trainers

Cinderella

hates the ball

Choose two fairy tales you know and make a star chart like the one above. Use your chart to write your new fairy tale. Although you are telling a different story, write in the same style as a traditional fairy tale, for example beginning *Once upon a time ...*
Also include some of the minor characters. How can they be changed?

Different perspectives

Learning objectives

Text level
- *To manipulate narrative perspective by writing a story with two different narrators.*
- *To plan quickly and effectively the plot, characters and structure of their own narrative writing.*

Activity Sheet/Expectations

The activity sheet focuses on character and perspective and provides a starting point for the development of what could become a sophisticated narrative (see 'Further activities' below).

The sheet is organised so that the character in question can be a boy or girl, Karl or Carla. (The situation outlined can fit either and the children can decide on the character for themselves.)

The starting point is a school report, which presents a mixed view of the character. Surrounding the report are comments from minor characters, most of which suggest a different perspective or hint at other factors. The children's task is to develop these perspectives so that the character becomes multifaceted. From this, the children are asked to write a character study. Useful phrases are given to help the children avoid writing in a confused or contradictory way. The character study can then, in turn, become the impetus for a narrative.

Further activities

Once the children have completed the character study, they should use it to provide the opening paragraphs of a story. Some planning will be needed, but since the children will know the character well by this time, they should try to make quick, useful notes. Prompt them to bear the following points in mind:

- In what ways do the character's traits suggest or affect the plot?
- How might the character respond to surprising or unpredictable events?
- How might the story conclude? What character traits would dominate?

The story can be written from two perspectives: the main character's and one other character's. For the second perspective, the children can choose from the minor characters given or create their own.

Resources

AS 'Points of view'

Points of view

Name: .... **Date:** ....

1. Below is the summary section of a school report. It does not say whether it is for a boy or girl, but you can decide whether it will be for Karl or Carla. Write the name at the top of the report and supply a surname of your own choice.

Summary Report for: ....
Often late. Always forgets PE kit. Must concentrate more. Homework slapdash. Forgot money for school trip. Enjoys reading and art and generally popular with other pupils. However, an unsatisfactory term.

That report just isn't true. I think …

Friend 1

Well some of it's true. For instance …

Friend 2

A wonderful athlete! Trains regularly and …

Coach

Oh dear, another bad report. But it's only to be expected since …

Grandmother

What a report! But I have to agree, except for …

Mother

Always reliable. A wonderful volunteer, especially …

RSPCA officer

2. Below the report are comments from other people who also know the character. Develop their comments on a separate sheet. Write notes, covering a range of points for each one.

3. Then choose the most interesting points about the character and write a detailed character study. Remember, you can include comments from the school report if you wish. To help you express yourself clearly, choose from these words and phrases:

| on the other hand | as well as | contrary | good side and bad side | contradiction |
| always | erratic | consistent | reliable/unreliable | as far as |

Playscripts

Learning objectives

Text level
- *To prepare a short section of story as a script, for example using stage directions, location/setting.*

Activity Sheet/Expectations

The activity sheet provides an example of prose that has also been written as a script. The children should note the differences between the two and develop the story in both text forms. Narrative texts undergo considerable reworking when adapted into scripts for performance and the children are not expected to grasp the full extent of this here. However, they do need to understand these essential points when making their notes:

- the story in a play is conveyed through dialogue;
- the stylistic conventions of a script are different from those of prose (such as the layout, which is set out for the actor and director to use);
- direct speech is used and speech marks are dropped;
- description in particular is lost from prose (of a setting for example) but can be conveyed through stage directions (perhaps depicting location);
- the description of a character's emotions in prose will be conveyed through dialogue and performance in a play;
- some elements will be lost when a story is written as a script, but others may be gained in performance.

These points are best understood if the play is acted out as well as simply being read aloud. Traditionally, a script was open to revision by the playwright during rehearsals and the children will be able to make clearer judgements if they can see and hear their scripts. For example, they would be unable to include crowds when performing the scene.

Further activities

The children could develop the story opening into a short narrative, with a single climax and resolution. As a separate piece of work they can then develop the scene into a play, following the main points of the narrative.

In small groups, the whole play or selected parts can be acted out and simple props devised. The work can be revised in performance and modifications made. The children should adopt different roles, such as director and stage manager as well as taking on acting roles.

Note: It is useful to have available narratives which are also scripts (see 'Resources'). The children can focus on particular scenes, noting what has been cut from the narrative and how this is conveyed in the script.

Resources

AS 'Things on my mind'; *A Kestrel for a Knave* by Barry Hines (Penguin); *Kes: The Play* by Barry Hines and Allan Stronach (Heinemann)

Things on my mind

Name: .... **Date:** ....

1. Read the following scene from a story entitled 'Things on my mind'.

Andy strolled across the school playground. He could feel the sun on his head. The heatwave was now in its third day and everybody was listless. Children were everywhere, sitting on benches or lying about on the grass. Lily, his twin sister, was making a daisy chain. Harry, his best friend, was sitting under a tree, pouring water from a bottle over his face. It was so hot hardly anybody was walking around.

"Andy!" Harry was waving. "Come here, I've saved you a shady spot."

"It won't be here for long, if you don't hurry up!" added Lily in her high-pitched voice.

"OK! I'll be there in a minute."

Andy turned and waved, but he carried on walking in the opposite direction. In the far corner of the playground he could see Todd. He was leaning against the wall. Even from this distance Andy could see the scowl on his face.

2. Now read the same scene as a script.

Things on my mind   Scene 1

A heatwave. Andy is strolling across the school playground. Most children are sitting on benches and lying on the grass. Harry is sitting under a tree, pouring water from a bottle over his face. Lily, Andy s twin sister, is making a daisy chain.

Harry: (*Waving*) Andy! Come here, I've saved you a shady spot.

Lily: It won't be here for long, if you don't hurry up!

Andy: (*Andy turns, waves back*) OK! I'll be there in a minute. (*But he walks on*)

Todd is leaning against a wall in the far corner of the playground.

3. Draw a table of two columns and head them 'Story' and 'Playscript'. List all the changes that have been made between the story and the playscript. Think about layout, punctuation and description.

4. Now write a comment saying what is lost from the story and how this might be conveyed in the play. Think about how the play could be performed. Can everything that is in the story be conveyed in the playscript? Add any other ideas for the performance.

5. Finish the scene in the story. Then write it as a playscript.

Using kennings to personify

Learning objectives

Text level
● *To write own poems experimenting with active verbs and personification; produce revised poems for reading aloud individually.*

Activity Sheet/Expectations

The kenning has its origin in Anglo-Saxon and Norse – *kenna* is from Old Norse and means 'know'. A kenning describes the attributes of something by replacing the name with a metaphor. A warrior could, for example, refer to his shield as a *death-banisher*. In 'The Lesser Spotted Yellow Ankle-Biter', Michael Taylor, a pupil, has created a poem around a kenning depicting a dog as an *ankle-biter*.

The children can use the poem to stimulate ideas. For example, they could develop a poem around a single kenning, rather than write poems made from a list of kennings. They could also personify the object or creature, giving it human or animal features. Initially, the children are asked to invent a series of kennings from which they can choose the one they like best. To do this effectively, it is useful if they write notes of particular characteristics. Making a star chart can be helpful. The one below identifies some possible features of a lorry and, in effect, personifies it.

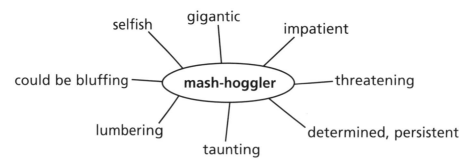

The children could also use the pronouns *he* or *she* in their poem, if they wish to reinforce the idea of personification.

Further activities

Poems can be written about a pair of kennings. For instance, the children could write a conversation poem between the lorry (*mash-hoggler*) and the road (*beast-breaker*), between a collar and lead or a parrot and a cage, and so on. Encourage them to choose pairs that can be explored fruitfully and which suggest situations or scenarios. For example, the parrot's relationship with its cage opens up questions about caged birds.

You might also like to look at some other Anglo-Saxon poetry and stories, for example those by Kevin Crossley-Holland.

Resources

AS 'A kenning'; examples of Anglo-Saxon writing, such as *Tales from the Old World* by Kevin Crossley-Holland (Orion)

A kenning

Name: .... **Date:** ....

1. Read this kenning by Michael Taylor.

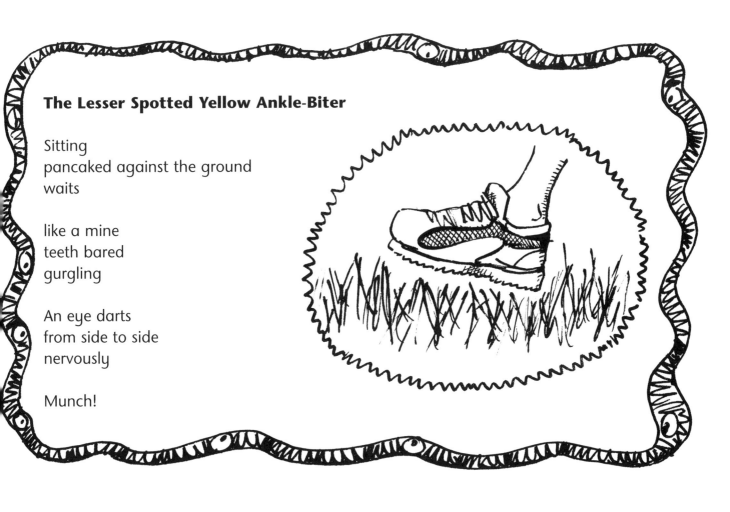

The Lesser Spotted Yellow Ankle-Biter

Sitting
pancaked against the ground
waits

like a mine
teeth bared
gurgling

An eye darts
from side to side
nervously

Munch!

2. What is the *lesser spotted yellow ankle-biter* and why is it a kenning?

3. Underline some of the interesting verbs used in the poem.

4. Make lots of your own kennings for different creatures and objects. Think of at least ten!
Try to experiment, for example a lorry could be a *route-trundler*, or it could become an
animal or person such as a *mash-hoggler*.

5. Choose your favourite kenning from the list and develop a poem about it. To help you
do this, write down the features that your animal or object has in a star chart. Refer to
your star chart as you write your poem. You could personify your creature – make it seem
like a person.

6. When you have finished, present your poem to the class.

Autobiography

Learning objectives

Text level
● To distinguish *between implicit and explicit points of view and how these can differ* in autobiography.

Activity Sheet/Expectations

The extract on the activity page is taken from Yasmin Alabhai-Brown's autobiography, *No Place Like Home*, which is largely concerned with her life in East Africa before Idi Amin's expulsion of the Asian community.

It is assumed that the children will already recognise some of the differences between biography and autobiography, such as the use of third and first person respectively, and also recognise the difference between fact, opinion and fiction. The focus on the activity sheet is a more challenging task: to be able to identify implicit meanings and perceive that the eye of the child is different from that of the adult. By focusing carefully on the text, the contradictions between the emotions the child feels on receiving a prize and the adult's sardonic view of the school system (which paid undue deference to the English system) should become apparent. For example, the adult voice in *A line of self-important Englishmen and women would sit through this, showing no emotion and inevitably mispronouncing the Asian and African names as they called out the next victim* contrasts with the child's *pride* when given *a book and a handshake*.

Further activities

The children could choose a historical figure to research, such as Shakespeare, and write two accounts of him or her – the first as a biography, the second as an autobiography. By taking on different roles, the children should be able to highlight the differences and similarities between the two. They could draw up a table to note these and include points such as the change of voice from the objective to the personal in the use of the first and third person, and the factual information common to both.

For children carrying out research in order to compose a biographical account, you might like to provide some suitable source material, for example *The Barefoot Book of Heroes* by Rebecca Hazell. This fascinating and accessible book details the lives of historical figures across cultures.

Resources

AS 'Elocution contests'; biographical accounts, such as *The Barefoot Book of Heroes* written and illustrated by Rebecca Hazell (Barefoot Books)

Elocution contests

Name: .... **Date:** ....

1. Yasmin Alabhai-Brown was brought up in Uganda but moved to Britain with her family during the 1970s, when the president at the time, Idi Amin, forced the Asian community to leave the country. Read the following extract which is taken from a description of her school life in Uganda.

My father was almost pleased for a short while then, as he saw me blossoming into a young girl who could recite entire chunks from the great English writers and who consistently won British Council elocution contests because unlike the other Asian children I could say 'p' and 't' with a proper puff. Six tedious hours, while seventy of us recited "Do you remember an Inn, Miranda ... ?" or even worse, good manners rhymes like

It is well to remember,
No elbows on the table please,
Nor is a cup, one understands,
So heavy that it needs both hands.

A line of self-important Englishmen and women would sit through this, showing no emotion and inevitably mispronouncing the Asian and African names as they called out the next victim. At the end, a brief statement would announce the three winners in the three categories and we would get a book and a handshake which thrilled us immeasurably and gave us pride to take back to our anxious parents who were not allowed to attend the events.

From No Place Like Home *by Yasmin Alabhai-Brown*

2. In this extract Yasmin, as an adult, is looking back at her childhood. How do you think she felt as a child about receiving a prize? Underline any words that give you clues.

3. How has her attitude changed when she looks back as an adult at these events? Again, underline any words that give you clues.

4. Use the work you have done to write two paragraphs explaining the difference between these two views.

Editorials

Learning objectives

Text level
- *To develop a journalistic style through considering: what is of public interest in events; the interest of the reader; selection and presentation of information.*
- To write an editorial.

Activity Sheet/Expectations

The article from *The Guardian*, 9 January 2001, reproduced on the activity sheet, has several features typical of a news report: a fast-paced style, a great of deal information packed into a small space and lengthy sentences with few pauses. Point these features out to the children.

It is assumed that the children will have had some experience of writing newspaper reports and the main focus here is on writing an editorial. To do this effectively, the children are asked to comment on issues raised in the report and to adopt a particular perspective. Several issues are presented which focus on the public interest – in particular, the balance between the need for children and young people to make decisions and become independent, and the need for a safe environment in which to do so. Other issues, such as the cost of the rescue and the danger to the firefighters, should also be considered.

The children should try to discuss as many issues as they can in their editorial but remind them to decide on the perspective they will take and the conclusions they will draw before they begin writing. It is best if they use the kind of written style suited to argument. Connectives related to logical thinking such as *however, having said that* and *consequently* are useful.

Further activities

The children can generate their own newspaper report about a real incident occurring locally and ask other class members to write an editorial about it. These can be selected for inclusion in a class newspaper.

Provide the children with a range of newspapers to study – local, tabloid and broadsheet. (These may need to be vetted first.) Ask the children to identify editorials and comments that interest them and which they can understand, and to note differences in style, the varying difficulty of the language used and the kinds of issues selected for comment.

Resources

AS 'Newspaper report'; broadsheet and tabloid newspapers

Newspaper report

Name: .... **Date:** ....

1. Read this newspaper report.

RESCUE DRAMA

Boys stuck in mud plucked to safety

Rebecca Allison

Two schoolboys came within inches of death after sinking up to their shoulders in freezing mud as they dug for worms.

Emergency services launched a dramatic rescue attempt to reach Stuart Duthie,14, and his friend Richard Ely,11, when they became trapped in the mud flats of the river Orwell, near Ipswich, Suffolk, while digging for fish bait.

The alarm was raised by a dog walker who heard the boys' screams as they sunk into the mud 150 metres from the riverbank on Sunday.

After several unsuccessful efforts to reach the pair using ropes and riot shields, firefighters managed to inch out on ladders and dig mud away from the boys to reduce pressure on their bodies. The boys, who were stuck for an hour, were freed and winched to safety by an RAF Sea King rescue helicopter. They were treated for mild hypothermia at Ipswich hospital.

Assistant Divisional Officer Karl Rolfe, of Suffolk fire service, said the pair were extremely lucky the tide was going out. "If the tide had been coming in we would have been involved in a race against time. It was a fairly lengthy and protracted operation to free them.

"We needed to use ladders because we could easily have sunk ourselves. We laid out our ladders in lines with boards underneath as staging posts to stop them sinking as we walked out. The boys were fairly calm – but they were very scared by the time we got them out. We had to take care not to injure them because of the suction from the mud."

He added the rescue should serve as a warning to others not to walk on to mud flats so far from shore.

From The Guardian
9 January 2001

2. An editorial is an article written by the editor giving an opinion about an event in the news.

Write an editorial comment on the above report. Think about the following issues first:

● Should the boys have been with adults?

● Should children be encouraged to be independent and go on trips alone?

● Were there any notices warning of the dangers? Who is responsible for these?

● Although dangerous, in what way was the incident a learning experience for the boys?

● What other points can you think of?

Inventing mnemonics

Learning objectives

Word level
● *To invent and use mnemonics for irregular or difficult spellings.*

Activity Sheet/Expectations

(You may wish to use this unit in connection with the unit 'Selling strategies', page 4.)

Mnemonics are an amusing and inventive way to recall spellings. However, they are not as easy to create as might first appear and sometimes it is more useful to use other spelling strategies. A mnemonic is best used with short words or the part of the word that gives trouble. Not only is it difficult to create a mnemonic for a lengthy word, it can be more difficult to remember than the spelling itself. Having said that, some children do create bizarre mnemonics that only they can remember. It is, in any case, best if children create their own mnemonics rather than have them imposed.

The activity sheet has two sections. In the first the children are asked to identify the part of a word that is likely to cause difficulty and to create a short mnemonic for this part only. In the second section they are given short but difficult spellings to create mnemonics for, before writing mnemonics for spellings they find tricky.

Although a mnemonic may be nonsense, it should be grammatically correct. That is to say, it should use connectives, phrases or sentences. It should not simply be a series of words strung together as these are unlikely to be remembered. The children should also be reminded that they do not have to spell the mnemonic, only recall it.

Below are some examples of mnemonics, but generally the children should have fun and be able to invent their own.

daisies	**d**ogs **a**nd **i**nky **s**pots
yacht	**y**aks **a**lways **c**arry **h**airy **t**ails
physics	**p**lease **h**ug **y**ellow **s**nails **i**n **c**osy **s**lippers
niece	**n**ancy **i**s **e**ating **c**reme **e**ggs

Further activities

The children could also try inventing simple rhymes to help them remember spellings and rules. The rhyme in the rule '*i* before *e* except after *c*' helps to make it memorable.

Resources

AS 'Mnemonics'

Mnemonics

Name: .... **Date:** ....

A mnemonic (pronounced 'nemonic') can help you remember a spelling or part of a spelling. For example, if you could not remember *meas* in the word *measure* you could invent a mnemonic to help you, like this:

my **e**lephant **a**lways **s**neezes

Every time you needed to spell *measure*, you could then think of the mnemonic.

1. Decide which part of the words below are difficult to remember and underline them. Then make up a mnemonic for each part.

> daisies   traveller   receipt   leisure
>
> recommendation   separate   disguise   business

2. Now work out mnemonics for each of these complete words.

> yacht   physics   ochre   gnome
>
> aisle   reign   chorus   guess

3. Think of five spellings you often get wrong. Invent mnemonics for them. For example:

nancy **is** **e**ating **c**reme **e**ggs = **niece**

Proverbs

Learning objectives

Word level
- *To collect and explain the meanings and origins of proverbs, referring to dictionaries of proverbs and other reference sources.*
- To study how poets subvert the meanings of proverbs.

Activity Sheet/Expectations

Poets such as Paul Muldoon and John Hegley have used proverbs to subvert meaning and create comic effects. Some knowledge of proverbs is needed to appreciate 'Symposium' fully. Contemporary children may be unaware of the proverbs included in the poem, although they can still appreciate the images in comic lines such as *For want of a nail the sky might fall.*

The children can use the poem as a model to write their own, drawing on common sayings they know. In addition, there may be children who know and use expressions and proverbs from other languages and cultures which they can share.

The purpose of the activity is, of course, to twist and subvert meanings to create a nonsense poem. This requires some sophistication. A useful start is to think of a saying or expression and change the beginning or ending by recording the first thing that comes into your head. A series of these can be made and the children can pick and choose the ones they like best to form the basis of a poem. They can then decide whether or not they wish to make their poem rhyme. The children could also guess why the poem is entitled 'Symposium' before they check in a dictionary.

Further activities

The children could study a range of nonsense poetry, comparing one poem with another to note how different effects are achieved. The work of Edward Lear and Lewis Carroll, for instance, has a melancholy tone or sense of loss in it.

The origins of nursery rhymes can be studied and nursery rhymes can also spark further ideas for poetry writing. Have dictionaries of proverbs and nursery rhymes available.

'Symposium' appears in *National Poetry Day Presents Comic Verse*. Included is a commentary by Paul Muldoon about classroom clichés, the way in which 'poetry can re-invent the commonplace', and the nonsensical rhyme scheme – and you may wish to share this with the class.

When reading poetry for children, John Hegley does a comic turn in which child members of the audience join him to complete the endings of proverbs that he begins. The result is inventive and nonsensical lines – and a useful activity for stimulating children's imaginations.

Resources

AS 'Proverb poem'; proverb and nursery rhyme dictionaries; *National Poetry Day Presents Comic Verse* (Forward Publishing, 1988)

Proverb poem

Name: .... **Date:** ....

1. Read this poem by Paul Muldoon.

Symposium

You can lead a horse to water but you can't make it hold
its nose to the grindstone and hunt with the hounds.
Every dog has a stitch in time. Two heads? You've been sold
one good turn. One good turn deserves a bird in the hand.

A bird in the hand is better then no bread.
To have your cake is to pay Paul.
Make hay while you can still hit the nail on the head.
For want of a nail the sky might fall.

People in glass houses can't see the wood
for the new broom. Rome wasn't built
between two stools.
Empty vessels wait for no man.

A hair of the dog is a friend indeed.
There's no fool like the fool
who's shot his bolt. There's no smoke after
the horse is gone.

2. Write your own nonsense poem using common sayings and any proverbs you know.
For example, does your mum or other relative have a special saying? Do you share any
sayings with friends?

You could also draw on songs, common expressions that comedians or celebrities use or
anything else you think is suitable. Remember, however, that you must change the
sayings to make a nonsense poem. Experiment and see what comic lines you can make.

Active and passive

Learning objectives

Sentence level
● *To investigate further the use of active and passive verbs: secure the use of the terms* active *and* passive; *know how sentences can be reordered by changing from one to the other; identify examples of active and passive verbs in texts; experiment in transformation from active to passive and vice versa and study the impact of this on meaning; consider how the passive voice can conceal the agent of a sentence.*

Activity Sheet/Expectations

In the active tense the subject is placed first, and in the passive the object is placed first. For example, *Lily found the purse* is in the active tense whereas *The purse was found by Lily* is in the passive tense. However the 'by phrase' can be concealed: *The purse was found*.

The use of the passive tense indicates a formal style but, in practice, texts do not fall neatly into one category or the other. Many include a mix of the two, though some, such as official or technological reports, will have a bias towards the passive.

In the activity sheet the children are asked to combine several skills. They must write Agent Bradshaw's log in the active tense and convert it into the passive for the official report. They also need to write a convincing account of Agent Bradshaw's disappearance. This is more challenging than, for example, completing exercises in which active sentences are converted into passive ones. In addition, placing the work in a text such as a log or report gives it greater coherence and allows the children to see in what context the passive, in particular, might be used. The children should be able to adopt the appropriate styles for the log and the report, but also to write naturally, so that the flow of ideas are not impeded. They can then compare the immediacy of the active tense with the more distant passive.

Further activities

As a further learning point the children can examine the official report and note where the passive text can be altered to conceal the (grammatical) agent, indicated through the 'by phrase'. For example, *by Director Jacques* and *by Coordinator Rockwell* have been removed from the following sentence, although they are implied: *He was given an investigation chip and debriefed.* The children can examine their own text to see if there are any other examples of this.

Fiction and non-fiction books can be selected at random and the children can try to spot sentences that use the 'by phrase', denoting the passive tense.

Resources

AS 'Agent Bradshaw's log'; fiction and non-fiction books

Agent Bradshaw's log

Name: .... **Date:** ....

1. Read the passage and log below.

Agent Bradshaw has disappeared. He belongs to Synchra, a worldwide investigation bureau that studies the events surrounding reported UFO sightings. Every agent must keep a coded log. The first page of Agent Bradshaw s log has been found and deciphered by Synchra.

Agent Bradshaw's Log
10 April 2010

Head Office, London Zone, called me at 5am. Director Jacques gave me an investigation chip and Coordinator Rockwell debriefed me. The chip detailed an incident in the Gobi Desert. Agent Sculshaw had recorded the incident at 4.10am on 9 April 2010. I agreed to catch the 7am plane to Datong from Terminal 8.

2. Write the second page of Agent Bradshaw's log in the active tense. You should write about 100 words explaining what has happened and why he has gone missing.

3. An official report must now be written about Agent Bradshaw's disappearance. It will contain his log. The first page has been rewritten in the passive tense. Rewrite the second page.

TOP SECRET
Reference: Bradshaw 1042010
Agent Bradshaw was called by Head Office, London Zone, at 5am. He was given an investigation chip by Director Jacques and debriefed by Coordinator Rockwell. An incident in the Gobi Desert was detailed in the chip. The incident had been recorded by Agent Sculshaw at 4.10am on 9 April 2010. It was agreed that Agent Bradshaw should catch the 7am plane to Datong from Terminal 8.

Using conditionals

Learning objectives

Sentence level
- *To investigate conditionals, for example using* if, then, might, could, would, *and their uses, for example in deduction, speculation, supposition.*
- *To explore use of conditionals in past and future, experimenting with transformations, discussing effects, for example speculating about possible causes (past), reviewing a range of options and their outcomes (future).*

Activity Sheet/Expectations

The activity sheet presents the children with a letter to an agony aunt, Debbie, from Lana who is unhappy at home, ostensibly because she does not get along with her older sister Becky. However, several other reasons for her unhappiness are implied and the children should recognise these (such as feeling neglected by her parents).

The children are asked to write a reply to the letter, in the guise of Debbie. This requires speculation, not only about future ways forward but also about possible causes for the situation that has arisen. To do this effectively the children should use various forms of the conditional.

Before beginning, the children can annotate the text if they wish, highlighting possible areas for discussion (such as the spare room).

The children should write about 300 words, in an informal style. They should organise their writing into coherent paragraphs and use connectives to link points (some of which would be conditionals). They should also explore as many possibilities as they can. For example, if speculating about the use of the spare room, they could include questions as well as statements, such as: *Would the family consider the possibility of putting the computer somewhere else? Would it help to talk to Simon about the difficulties you are experiencing?* Once the letters are completed, the children could discuss them with a partner and modify them in the light of 'Further activities'.

Further activities

The children could also write a letter from Becky to Debbie, presenting a different perspective on the situation.

Ask the children to collect letters to agony aunts (and uncles!) from comics and teenage magazines. They could use these to speculate about answers to the problems presented, again using the conditional.

Resources

AS 'Problem page'; sample agony aunt letters

Problem page

Name: .... **Date:** ....

1. Read this letter to an agony aunt.

Dear Debbie,

I have a problem! It's my older sister, Becky.
I have to share a room with her and we don't
get on. I can't get my homework done
because she plays her guitar all the time. If
I ask her to lower the sound she shouts at me.
We quarrel all the time and she blames me for
everything.

For instance, last week one of her favourite CDs
went missing. She immediately assumed I'd taken it. She told Mum I'd
borrowed it without permission and Mum believed her. (She always
does!) When I was questioned about it, I knew Mum didn't think I was
telling the truth. The next day Becky found the CD in my brother
Simon's room, but she didn't say anything. Neither did Mum. Becky
hasn't apologised to me and I don't think she ever will. Dad won't get
involved. He says we have to learn to work things out between
ourselves.

We do have a spare room, but it has the computer in it. Everyone is
supposed to use it, but Simon and Dad are usually on it, so I hardly ever
get a go.

Mum takes Becky's side and Dad takes Simon's and I'm just piggy in
the middle. That's what it's like in our house. I'm so unhappy, I feel like
running away. What should I do?

Yours truly,

Lana West

2. Write Debbie's reply to Lana, exploring all the things she could do to make her situation better. Think about what has happened to Lana as well as what could happen in the future.

Use conditionals such as *if, then, might, could, would* and *should* in your reply.

Conveying the passing of time

Learning objectives

Text level
- *To understand aspects of narrative structure, for example how the passing of time is conveyed to the reader.*
- *To write own story using, for example flashbacks.*

Activity Sheet/Expectations

George Eliot (Mary Ann Evans) was one of the leading thinkers of her time and had a clear understanding of how economic, cultural and social conditions shaped lives. *The Mill on the Floss* was published in 1860 and called into question Victorian conventions and values, particularly those relating to women and girls.

The children are asked to study a short, well-crafted extract from the conclusion, which is set five years after the disastrous flood. (The subsequent paragraphs have not been included in case the children want to read the book.) The narrator is reflecting on previous events in the novel and the passing of time is conveyed through words and phrases that:

- suggest the past: *echoes, this history,*;
- set the scene in the present: *hopeful lading, was still living*;
- make the connection between the two: *five years after, the fifth autumn*.

Repetition is used to emphasise renewal (*Nature repairs her ravages*), but also to convey loss (*Nature repairs her ravages – but not all*), while the last line suggests experience and the wisdom it can bring. The organisation of the paragraphs stresses the central paragraph, which also connects the past with the present. You may also wish to point out that the landscape and nature are both a force for healing and change.

In the Victorian novel the narrator is foregrounded and strong, so the reader trusts the voice. The children should try to capture this strong, reflective voice in their own writing.

Further activities

The children can use the paragraphs they have written to spark ideas for an extended story. They may need to write several paragraphs to create one that has sufficient impact and has the seeds of a good plot. They can then use timelines to work out a rough structure for their stories, marking and improving parts or chapters.

Encourage the children to read *The Mill on the Floss*. It is accessible to confident and able readers, and while they may not understand all the passages, they will be carried by the characters and story. It will also give them an insight into the values and conventions of the Victorian period.

Resources

AS 'Time passing'; *The Mill on the Floss* by George Eliot (Penguin Classics)

Time passing

Name: .... Date: ....

1. Read this extract from *The Mill on the Floss* by George Eliot (1817–90).

Nature repairs her ravages – repairs them with her sunshine, and with human labour. The desolation wrought by that flood had left little visible trace on the face of the earth, five years after. The fifth autumn was rich in golden corn-stacks, rising in thick clusters among the distant hedgerows; the wharves and warehouses on the Floss were busy again, with echoes of eager voices, with hopeful lading[1] and unlading.

And every man and woman mentioned in this history was still living – except those whose end we know.

Nature repairs her ravages – but not all. The uptorn trees are not rooted again; the parted hills are left scarred: if there is a new growth, the trees are not the same as the old, and the hills underneath their green vesture bear the marks of the past rending. To the eyes that have dwelt on the past, there is no thorough repair.

[1]lading means to load

2. This extract could come from the end or at the beginning of a story. Try to explain why for both cases.

3. Underline some words in black that tell you that the narrator is thinking about the past.

4. Underline some words in red that tell you the scene is set in the present.

5. Which words suggest both the past and the present? Underline them in blue.

6. What do you think *Nature repairs her ravages* refers to? What effect does repeating it have? How has the phrase been changed the second time?

7. What do you think the last line means? Why might it be important?

8. There are three paragraphs. Why do you think this is?

9. Write the ending to a story you have not yet written! It can also be the beginning, when the narrator is looking back at events that have happened. Imagine a scene in your mind's eye where something important has taken place. Use the extract above to help you, as though you are thinking to yourself and talking to the reader at the same time.

MAE6

Playing with meaning

Learning objectives

Text level
● *To investigate how poets play with meanings.*

Activity Sheet/Expectations

The American poet May Swenson (1919–1989) has an eye for the unusual, cleverly exploited in 'Cardinal Ideograms'. The structure of the poem can be used by children as a model, but it is suggested that they focus on symbols other than numbers, such as letters of the alphabet, mathematical or keyboard symbols or alternative ones of their own choice. (You might like to explain that a *lorgnette* is a pair of spectacles mounted on to one side handle.)

Providing a structure allows the children to focus on creating their own definitions. These should be inventive and quirky and the children should have plenty of opportunities to experiment with language. Initially they are given some help. They are asked to think of definitions for *X, Y* and *Z* and can practice writing these in different ways so that a range of shapes are made, from which might spring unique ideas and associations. Since the presentation of the poem will be a key to the definitions, the children will also need to perfect the layout and think about the way in which form relates to meaning. Dictionaries and thesauruses should be available.

Further activities

Encourage the children to recognise how word associations can be made. For instance, a word in a poem can have connotations through meaning and sound. In the fifth stanza of Tennyson's 'The Lady of Shalott', the rhymes *loom, room, bloom* and *plume* occur but not *doom*. Similarly, *wide, side* and *cried* occur, but not *died*. Whether or not these words actually come to mind when the poem is read, they still resonate powerfully in the stanza.

The children can also play a word association game using word chains. One word is said which sparks another, and so on. It can be played using particular parts of speech only, such as verbs. Further activities in making associations are suggested on the activity sheet.

May Swenson has a well-tuned ear and much of her poetry is musical. If possible, make available more of her poems (see 'Resources').

Resources

AS 'A poem from 0 to 10'; dictionaries and thesauruses; poems by May Swenson, such as: 'Cat and the Weather', 'Feel Like a Bird' in *To Mix with Time* (Charles Scribner's Sons) or 'The Centaur' in *The New Oxford Book of Children's Verse* edited by Neil Philip (Oxford)

A poem from 0 to 10

Name: .... **Date:** ....

1. Read this poem by May Swenson.

Cardinal Ideograms

0 A mouth. Can blow or breathe, be funnel, or Hello.

1 A grass blade or a cut.

2 A question seated. And a proud bird's neck.

3 Shallow mitten for two-fingered hand.

4 Three-cornered hut on one stilt. Sometimes built so the roof gapes.

5 A policeman. Polite Wearing visored cap.

6 O unrolling, tape of ambiguous length on which is written the mystery of everything curly.

7 A step, detached from its stair.

8 The universe in diagram: A cosmic hourglass. (Note enigmatic shape, absence of any valve of origin, how end overlaps beginning.) Unknotted like a shoelace and whipped back and forth, can serve as a model of time.

9 Lorgnette for the right eye. In England or if you are Alice The stem is on the left.

10 A grass blade or a cut companioned by a mouth. Open? Open. Shut? Shut.

2. Use the poem as a model to write your own, but think of symbols that are not numbers.

3. Practise first. For example, think of definitions for X, Y and Z. Write the letters in different ways and see what ideas they spark. Think of unusual definitions. Can you guess what a *lorgnette* is from the way it is described in the poem?

4. You could then:
- develop X, Y and Z into a poem (for example, think about where they come in the alphabet and how you might pair them with A, B and C);
- or you could use other symbols such as keyboard symbols. What associations do these symbols have when you see them?

MAE6

Stock characters

Learning objectives

Text level
- *To identify the key features of different types of literary text, for example stock characters* (the villain).

Activity Sheet/Expectations

The extract on the activity sheet is taken from Leon Garfield's rewriting of 'Othello' for children in *Shakespeare's Stories*, and describes Iago's villainous and deceitful nature. The quality of the writing is such that the children can learn a great deal about shaping the character of a villain and they can use the extract as a model to write their own character sketch.

First of all, however, the children are asked to respond to the text by isolating the feelings it conjures up and noting which particular words and phrases make Garfield's Iago memorable. The children should identify that:

- he is deceitful – *Then his brow darkened, and all pleasantry slipped from his face*;
- his motives involve revenge – *as thoughts of how he might obtain his revenge flickered through his mind*;
- he plots – *He began to pace to and fro, muttering to himself.*

The final lines indicate that Iago will begin to poison Othello's mind, by suggesting falsely that Othello's wife, Desdemona, and Cassio, his lieutenant, are lovers.

The children should draw vivid character sketches and may wish to include a description of the character's appearance. If so, they should try to create a visual image that does not conform to the typical one.

Further activities

The children could use their completed character studies as a basis for their own stories, where the villain's motive or motives form the plot.

If possible, the children should read Leon Garfield's story of Othello and consider what other aspects of Iago are revealed.

The children could also compare the structure of the narrative with that of the play by studying the end of Act I in Shakespeare's *Othello*. This concerns Iago's speech, which is the subject of the extract, the final line being the same in both.

Resources

AS 'Iago'; if possible, have available *Shakespeare's Stories II* by Leon Garfield (Puffin)

Iago

Name: .... **Date:** ....

1. Leon Garfield wrote several of Shakespeare's plays in narrative form for children. Read the description below, which is taken from 'Othello' and presents a picture of the character Iago.

As Roderigo hastened away, Iago stared thoughtfully after him. He grinned amiably, and murmured: "Thus do I ever make my fool my purse." Then his brow darkened, and all pleasantry slipped from his face. Only hatred remained, hatred for the Moor [Othello]. He had confided in Roderigo that he hated the Moor because he had promoted Cassio over him; but there was another reason that was far stronger. He suspected that Othello had slept with his wife. He had no proof of this; he had only suspicion based on rumour. But it was enough. He told no one, because he was not a man who could endure being laughed at. He kept it within himself where it grew and grew like an ulcer on his soul. His very veins ran with poison. He began to pace to and fro, muttering to himself as thoughts of how he might obtain his revenge flickered through his mind. The Moor was an open man and trusted him; so much the worse for the Moor. Cassio was a handsome fellow, and spendthrift of his charm; so much the worse for Cassio. "Let me see ... after some time, to abuse Othello's ear, that he is too familiar with his wife ..." Suddenly he ceased his pacings. He laughed aloud and slapped his knee in triumphant delight.

"I ha't, it is engendered," he cried; "Hell and night must bring this monstrous birth to the world's light!"

2. What kind of character is Iago? How do you know?

3. Underline the words and phrases that show he is:
● deceitful
● determined
● full of revenge
● plotting something.

4. What do you think he plans to do?

5. What words create the greatest impression and why?

6. Now create your own villain. Consider all the features above and think about the villain's motives (reasons) for acting the way he or she does. Include other features as you wish.

Parody

Learning objectives

Text level
- *To identify how particular texts undermine, for example through parody.*
- *To parody a literary text.*

Activity Sheet/Expectations

Parody has its own traditions and writers have used it for generations to make satirical and political points, or simply to amuse. In poetry, established genres such as the sonnet or epic are often parodied, as are those poems that have entered the canon (for example Wordsworth's 'Daffodils').

The children may or may not have heard of 'The Song of Hiawatha', so on the activity sheet the parody is set against some lines from the original. This will allow the children to make comparisons. They should be able to identify the following key features:

- the shared rhythm;
- the shared rhyme scheme;
- the way the structure of the lines is mimicked;
- the way in which the repetition is exaggerated to accentuate humour.

In particular, the children need to recognise that a parody must be instantly recognisable to the reader and it is the form of the poem that creates this instant recognition. They also need to explore the way in which parody trivialises the serious.

The children can write their own parody using what they have learned and imitating Hiawatha or a classic poem of their own choice.

Further activities

Make available other verses from 'The Song of Hiawatha' for the children to read (see 'Resources' below). Though less popular than it used to be – the poem was part of the curriculum for many generations – it is still accessible and a story well worth reading.

Ask the children to carry out a survey amongst about thirty adults (from twenty years old) to find out how many have heard of 'The Song of Hiawatha'. They can classify the results according to age and see what useful information can be extrapolated from the results.

You might like to show the children colour plates in 'Hiawatha's Departure' (see 'Resources') and read the poem together. If it is available, you might also like to read 'Hiawatha's Childhood' (see 'Resources').

Resources

AS 'Hiawatha'; *The Illustrated Poets: Henry Wadsworth Longfellow*, selected by Geoffrey Moore and in which 'Hiawatha's Departure' appears (Aurum Press); *A Puffin Book of Verse*, compiled by Eleanor Graham in which 'Hiawatha's Childhood' appears (Puffin Books)

Hiawatha

Name: .... **Date:** ....

1. Read the two poems below.

Hiawatha s Childhood

Then Iagoo, the great boaster,
He the marvellous story-teller,
He the traveller and the talker,
He the friend of old Nokomis,
Made a bow for Hiawatha:
From a branch of ash he made it,
From an oak-bough made the arrows,
Tipped with flint, and winged with feathers,
And the cord he made of deer-skin.

From The Song of Hiawatha *by Henry Wadsworth Longfellow (1807—82)*

The Modern Hiawatha

When he killed the Mudjokivis,
Of the skin he made him mittens,
Made them with the fur side inside,
Made them with the skin side outside,
He, to get the warm side inside
Put the inside skin side outside;
He, to get the cold side outside,
Put the warm side fur side inside.
That's why he put the fur side inside,
Why he put the skin side outside,
Why he turned then inside outside.

From The Song of Milkanwatha *by George A Strong*

2. The second poem is a parody. What do you think a parody is ?

3. In what ways are the poems similar? Study the rhythm and rhyme and look for other common features. Make some notes of the main points.

4. How are the two poems different? Think about the different ways you would read them.

5. Write your own parody. You can imitate 'Hiawatha' or another poem, such as 'Daffodils' by William Wordsworth. Make sure you choose a classic poem that most people would know.

Writing an argument

Learning objectives

Text level
● *To construct effective arguments: developing a point logically and effectively; illustrating points persuasively; anticipating possible objections; harnessing the known views, interests and feelings of the audience; tailoring the writing to formal presentation where appropriate.*

Activity Sheet/Expectations

In the activity sheet 'A tricky question' the children are asked to make a difficult choice, selecting the most important from friendship, money and health. They need to weigh up different positions and present an argument justifying their perspective. This is challenging, since they must try to hold more than one point in their mind at a time. To do this, they are given some help to encourage coherent thinking and a logical shifting between the points.

In particular, by considering the issues in question 3 on the activity sheet, the children can cover several possibilities, visualise situations and decide which feature is the most important. The following questions and answers show how the children might proceed when considering friendship:

Q: Without friendship, what might happen?

A: *Without friendship, we might be sad and lonely.*

Q: Without friendship, would the other things (such as money) make up for it? If so, how?

A: *Money might not make up for this, since we would have no one to share it with.*

Q: Without friendship, would the other things (such as health) be affected? How?

A: *Health might be affected if we were sad.*

In this way the children can work through their ideas, eliminating the least important issues.

Help is given on setting out the argument clearly in writing. Some connectives and rhetorical devices are suggested to help the children present their arguments, but it is assumed that they will be familiar with many of these by now and be able to follow their points through.

Further activities

The children can present opposing arguments in a class debate or group discussion, and take questions to answer. One might select friendship as the most important, another money or health. A vote can then be taken.

Resources

AS 'A tricky question'

A tricky question

Name: .... **Date:** ....

1. What could you not do without? Below are three things that we all need. You must choose one that is more important than all the others and write an argument saying why. Below are tips about how to present your argument.

2. Before you write your argument make notes saying why each one is important.

3. Study your list and try to eliminate two of the things. Do this by asking yourself these questions:
● Without this, what might happen?
● Without this, would the other things make up for it? If so, how?
● Without this, would the other things be affected? How?

4. Now write your argument:
● In the introduction discuss the importance of friendship, money and health.
● Follow this by writing two more paragraphs saying which is the most important and why, comparing it with the others and giving examples to show what you mean.
● In the conclusion summarise the most important points you have made and appeal to the reader, for example you could say: "I am sure we would all agree that ..."
● Use connectives to develop your argument, such as *In addition, Consequently, However, On the other hand, Some might say ... but, Finally.*

Writing a balanced report

Learning objectives

Text level
- *To write a balanced report of a controversial issue; summarising fairly the competing views; analysing strengths and weaknesses of different issues.*

Activity Sheet/Expectations

The activity page focuses on the issue of child stars and whether or not children should be allowed to become celebrities. (You might like to use this unit in conjunction with the previous unit, in which the children are asked to select one position in an argument.)

The children should be able to identify with the issues and present a balanced argument in writing. However, they need to elaborate on the comments made, and to do this effectively, a process is suggested on the activity sheet. Further points on this process are made here:

- Firstly, the children need to divide the comments into those in favour of the case and those against. A 'For and Against' table will allow them to do this.
- Secondly, they should add any additional comments of their own on either side of the argument, for example *The child star usually has a disrupted education. On the other hand, if it is properly managed, the child may be financially secure for life.*
- Thirdly, the children should look for the strengths and weaknesses in the arguments on both sides. In answer to E they could consider the argument that, with determination, real talent will usually emerge.
- Next, the children should point to hypothetical or real examples to support what they say. (An example is given on the activity sheet.)
- Finally, they should plan their report, to include an introduction to the topic and a series of paragraphs addressing the points they have selected. The conclusion should draw main ideas together.

Some connectives are suggested on the activity sheet to encourage the children to write logically, but they should also think of their own.

Further activities

Discuss the use of rhetorical devices which are frequently used in argument, orally and in writing. The children can record phrases such as *We all know that, We would all agree.*

The children might like to organise a class debate around the issue of child celebrities and take a vote.

Resources

AS 'Child stars'

Child stars

1. Read these comments on whether or not children should become celebrities.

A

Children as well as adults will always want fame. You can't stop it.

B

I'm a child and I don't want fame! I'd rather have a normal life with some privacy and be a child.

C

I'm not against child stars, but they need the law to protect them.

D

I think fame cuts you off from your friends. They don't know how to treat you.

E

You shouldn't suppress talent. The opportunity may never come again.

F

Most child stars don't become adult stars. Then they're lost and unhappy.

2. Write an report that shows you are neither for nor against the issue. This means you will need to:

● consider all the points and add your own

● decide on the strengths and weaknesses of each point

● select the main points

● think of examples to support what you say. For instance, when considering C you could suggest that most of the child's earnings must be kept in a fund until the child is an adult. Include an introduction and conclusion in your report and divide it into paragraphs. Use terms such as *On one hand, While I agree.*

Extending vocabulary

Learning objectives

Word level
● *To practise and extend vocabulary.*

Activity Sheet/Expectations

The message in the speech bubbles on the activity sheet tells the reader to avoid using 'big words' by doing the very thing it cautions against. This is a humorous way for children to extend their vocabulary and use their ingenuity at the same time.

The children are asked to work out the meaning of 'Don't use big words' first. They could do this alone or in pairs, but when they come to write their own messages it is useful if they have a partner of similar ability to whom they can deliver their message. Roughly translated, the three sentences in the message read: *When giving your views, don't be pompous. Use clear language. Avoid slick phrases, obvious or otherwise.*

The children will need to have dictionaries, thesauruses and CD-ROMs available, both to work out the meaning of the vocabulary in 'Don't use big words' and to write their own sentences. Part of the skill is choosing the word which best fits the context, and this will be challenging, since the children may not have come across most of the words before simply from lack of experience. You may be interested to find out how many words they do recognise, so it is suggested they do this before using a dictionary. They should also use the context to try to read between the lines.

Further activities

Ask the children to list colloquialisms, popular sayings or imperatives and to rewrite these in overblown language.

The children can also choose some words, up to say ten, and investigate their etymology.

Resources

AS 'Don't use big words'; etymological dictionaries of proverbs and thesauruses; computer for CD-ROM/Internet research

Don't use big words

Name: .... **Date:** ....

1. Read the text in the speech bubble.

> In promulgating your esoteric cogitations, or articulating your superficial sentimentalities and amicable, philosophical or psychological observations, beware of platitudinous ponderosity. Let your conversational communications possess a clarified conciseness, a compacted comprehensibleness, coalescent consistency, and a concatenated cogency. Shun double entendres, prurient jocosity, and pestiferous profanity, obscurant or apparent.

Anonymous

2. What do you think this message means? Read the three sentences again and try to work out as much as you can from the words you know.

3. Now use a dictionary to find out the meaning of selected words, then guess the others.

4. Write down three short sentences in simple vocabulary to explain the message.

5. Write your own message using complicated language and give it to a partner to work out. Choose a straightforward message to start with, for example: 'Please shut the door'.

6. Write replies to each other, again using complicated words.

MAE6

Creating word games

Learning objectives

Word level
● *To practise and extend vocabulary, for example through inventing word games.*

Activity Sheet/Expectations

Here the children are asked to create a word game for others to solve, where one letter of the starter word changes in each move, until finally a new word is created that has none of the original letters in the same place. They also need to provide clues for each new word. An example is given on the activity sheet involving four-letter words. The children are then given a series of four- and five-letter words to change. (Changing the five-letter words will take considerably longer.) The children should keep their answers and work out how to present the starter word and clues, while ensuring that their clues are intelligible but not too easy.

Some examples are given below. The children may find other ways, although they must check these conform to the rules set out on the activity sheet.

bolt	belt, beat, bean, mean
post	pest, pelt, felt, fell
comb	come, came, tame, tape
pair	lair, laid, land, lend
plume	plums, slums, slams, slabs, stabs
skate	slate, slats, slits, flits, flips

The children will gain some insight into the way in which consonant digraphs such as *fl, sl, lt* and *nd*, and double letters such as *ll*, set limitations on word changes.

Note: You may wish to make dictionaries and spelling lists available when the children are working with five-letter words. You might also like to look at other examples of language play and word fun (see 'Resources').

Further activities

The children can design a range of games involving anagrams (for example *ogre – gore*), palindromes (for example *time – emit*) and other word games to create a booklet. Allow the children to design their booklets, word games, and questions and answers on the computer to maximise the impact of their work.

Resources

AS 'One at a time'; dictionaries; computers for DTP work; Folens *Spelling Programme, File 6*

One at a time

Name: .... **Date:** ....

1. Look at how the word *wash* can be changed.

wash ⟶ **c**ash ⟶ co**s**h ⟶ cos**t** ⟶ co**l**t

You will see that one letter at a time is changed to make a new word, so that by the last move a word is made that contains none of the original letters (in the same place).

To complete the word game, clues are needed for each move. Here are clues for the above words:

cash   Money, money, money!

cosh   You could be hit over the head with this!

cost   We all complain that it's too much to pay.

colt   This horse will be lively!

2. Now change the words below in the same way. Keep the answers and write clues to match.

Remember, in four-letter words you make four changes, in five-letter words you make five changes. If you need to, you can use the same letters but they must not be in the same place.

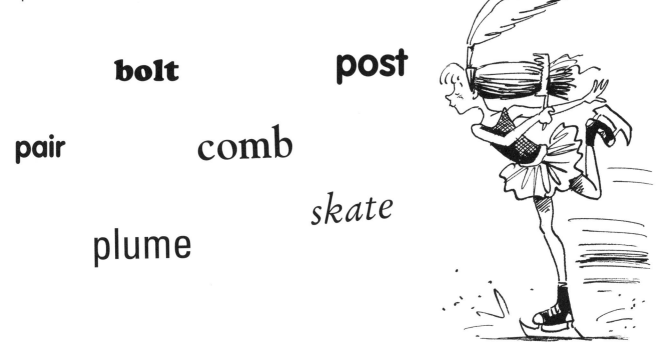

bolt   **post**

pair   **comb**

skate

plume

3. Design a way of presenting the starter words, clues and answers for other children to solve. You might like to use ICT.

Creating jokes

Learning objectives

Word level
● *To experiment with language, for example creating jokes.*

Activity Sheet/Expectations

Here the children are asked to embellish a 'shaggy dog story' further and then write their own. The tasks will require some command of the style and an awareness that this kind of joke, like most, is partly dependent on delivery for its humour. Consequently they need to take into account that the joke is told in the present tense, which creates immediacy, and that sometimes the listener is addressed directly as in *yes – you've guessed it*.

The children also need to be aware that non-standard English is used, for example colloquial speech (*Are you back again?*), sayings (*sure as eggs*) and slang (*scarpers*). However, jokes are not simply speech and they do have their own structure. Shaggy dog stories often use repetition, as well as language that rambles, in order to delay the surprise ending. Providing the children have a good command of English, they will be able to mimic these features instinctively, after they read the joke on the activity sheet.

If the children are not sure about any of the terms used, such as *punch line*, they should check in a dictionary first.

Further activities

Ask the children to create a joke book. They can collect different kinds of jokes, such as those mentioned on the activity sheet, and use them as models to create their own, which can be added to their books.

The children can also create riddles for each other, using puns and rhyme. The following is based the double meaning of *star*:

I may shine bright in Hollywood,
Las Vegas, London, Bollywood.
Like me, a luminous, fire sprite,
My cousin never sleeps at night.

If possible, provide copies of *The Ha Ha Bonk Book* for the children to read (see 'Resources'). This entertaining book contains a wide range of jokes. The children might also be able to buy their own joke books from newsagents and stationers.

Resources

AS 'Have you heard the one about … '; dictionaries; *The Ha Ha Bonk Book* by Janet and Allan Ahlberg (Puffin Books)

Have you heard the one about ... ?

Name: .... **Date:** ....

1. Jokes are rather like riddles. Most people cannot work out the answers. If you could, half
the fun would be lost. There are all kinds of jokes. There are quick-fire jokes, which follow
rapidly in succession and which some stand-up comedians use, shaggy dog stories that
seem to go on for ever, puns that depend on double meanings, visual jokes found in
pictures and others that simply play with words. Read the joke below.

A rabbit goes into a hardware store.
"Have you got any carrots?" he asks the shopkeeper.
"No, we don't sell carrots," says the shopkeeper.
So the rabbit leaves.

The next day the rabbit goes back to the shop.
"Have you got any carrots?" he asks the shopkeeper.
"I told you yesterday – we don't sell carrots. Go away."
Off the rabbit goes. But, sure as eggs, the next day
he's back.

"Have you got any carrots?" he asks the shopkeeper.
"Are you back again? WE DON'T SELL CARROTS!" says
the shopkeeper.
The rabbit clears off, but the next day – yes – you've
guessed it.

"Have you got any carrots?" he asks the shopkeeper.
"If you ask me that once more, I'll nail your ears to the
counter!" says the shopkeeper.
The rabbit scarpers fast, but next day there he is, the
same as usual.

"Have you got any nails?" he asks the shopkeeper.
"NO!" replies the shopkeeper.
"Have you got any carrots?"

2. The joke above is a shaggy dog story that could be developed further. Add more to it
(perhaps some irrelevant details, such as what the rabbit is wearing) but keep the spirit of
the joke and the repetition. Practise telling it to a friend in the best voice you can find.

3. Now write a shaggy story of your own that has a punch line at the end.

Plans and directions

Learning objectives

Sentence level
- *To revise the language conventions and grammatical features of the different types of texts such as: instructional texts, for example instructions and directions.*

Activity Sheet/Expectations

The activity sheet presents the children with an incomplete interior plan of a gallery, which has more than one level. The main purpose is for the children to create a set of working directions for finding the way around the building. The children should complete the plan of level 1 by including the features listed on the activity sheet and design a plan for level 2 that will be compatible with level 1. The children are also asked to decide whether or not they will use labels and/or symbols and what stylistic conventions to use, for example abbreviated sentences. Below is an example of the completed plans and directions.

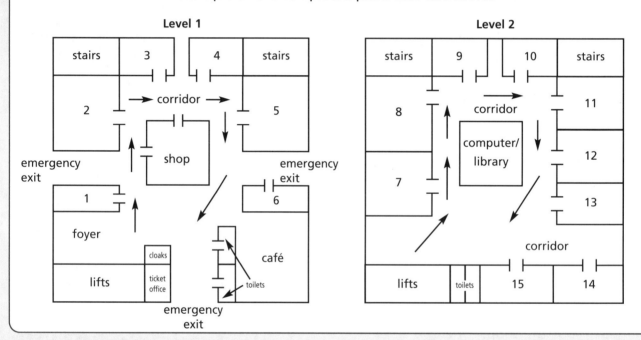

Further activities

Encourage the children to present their completed plans using ICT. They can then devise a plan and directions for getting around their own school for visitors to use. The children will no doubt have encountered several problems and overcome these during the making of the plan. They could then draw up a leaflet of 'Dos and Don'ts' focusing on what makes a good set of instructions.

Provide the children with opportunities to study plans of interiors of museums, libraries or galleries. They can assess the merits of the plans and identify any useful information.

Resources

AS 'This way or that'; computer for ICT work; plans of museum and library interiors

This way or that?

Name: .... **Date:** ....

1. Below is an incomplete plan of a gallery that is given to visitors so they can find their way around. You will see that it is designed for more than one level. Study it carefully.

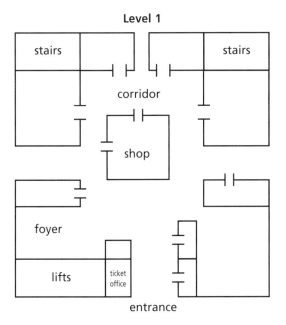

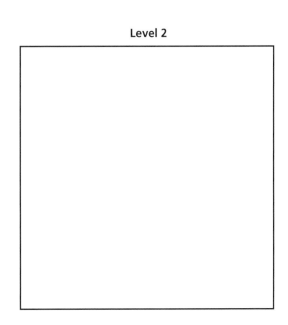

2. Complete level 1 by:
● numbering the exhibition rooms;
● devising a one-way system;
● adding three emergency exits;
● adding a café, cloakroom, toilet and shop.

3. Design level 2 to include:
● exhibition rooms;
● a one-way system;
● a computer room and library.

Your plan should be kept to one side of A4 and to scale, and have simple labels and/or symbols.

Any other information should be short and concise.

4. Now select one room on Level 2 and write some instructions to guide a partially-sighted visitor to reach it easily.

Regional speech

Learning objectives

Sentence level
- *To conduct detailed language investigations through reading, for example dialect.*

Text level
- *To annotate passages in detail in response to specific questions.*

Activity Sheet/Expectations

The extract on the activity sheet from *A Very Honorable Guy* is taken from a collection of short stories by the American writer, Damon Runyan. It is typical of his comic style and his ability to create characters through regional speech (whether realistic or embellished). It is also ideal for demonstrating to the children how the use of the vernacular can be crucial in the narration of a novel or short story. The distinctive narrator's voice and the description of characters immediately brings to mind other writers, such as Dickens, who also use exaggeration.

On the activity sheet the children are asked to read the extract in an New York-American accent, as far as they are able. They are then asked to study a standard English version of the first sentence and to comment on the changes. They should be able to see how dependent the story is on idiom. In particular the following is lost:

- the distinctive narrator's voice;
- the depiction of place (Brooklyn, New York);
- the fast-paced delivery;
- the character of Feet Samuels.

The children are asked to rewrite the next sentence themselves. This should give them further insight into the way in which crucial features are lost. Finally, they are asked to write a commentary suggesting when it is best to use regional speech in writing.

Further activities

The children could study short extracts from other writers such as Dickens to see how they use dialect to create effects, for example the character of Sam Weller in *Pickwick Papers*. They might also consider why some characters have no dialect, but speak in standard English regardless of their circumstances.

Show the children poems by a range of poets who use English dialects in different ways (see 'Resources'). They could also create their own stories and dialect poems, preferably using speech they are familiar with. They can note in what circumstances it is necessary to exaggerate (for example, for comic effect) and when regional speech needs to be recorded accurately (for example, to create realism.)

Resources

AS 'A very Honorable Guy'; *Duppy Jamboree* by Valerie Bloom (Cambridge); *Funky Chicken* and *Talking Turkeys* by Benjamin Zephaniah (Puffin Books)

A Very Honorable Guy

Name: .... **Date:** ....

1. Try to read the following to yourself in an American (New York) accent.

> Off and on I know Feet Samuels a matter of eight or ten years, up and down Broadway, and in and out, but I never have much truck with him because he is a guy I consider no dice. In fact, he does not mean a thing.
>
> In the first place, Feet Samuels is generally broke, and there is no percentage in hanging around brokers. The way I look at it, you are not going to get anything off a guy who has not got anything. So while I am very sorry for brokers, and am always willing to hope that they get hold of something, I do not like to be around them. Long ago an old-timer who knows what he is talking about says to me:
>
> "My boy," he says, "always try to rub up against money, for if you rub up against money long enough, some of it may rub off on you."
>
> *From* A Very Honorable Guy *by Damon Runyon*

2. What kind of character does the narrator's voice conjure up? What do you think he does for a living? What does he look like? Think of any characters in American films or television that remind you of the narrator.

3. Now read the first sentence again, this time written in standard English.

> I have known Feet Samuels for about eight or ten years around Broadway, but I've never had much to do with him because he is a man that I consider of no importance.

4. Try writing the next sentence in standard English yourself.

5. What has happened to the sentences? How has the narrator's voice changed? Underline some of the vocabulary changes in red and the verb tenses in black. What has happened to the verbs? What else do you notice?

6. Write a commentary, saying when it is best for regional speech to be used in writing.

Linked images

Learning objectives

Text level
- *To discuss how linked poems relate to one another by themes, format and repetition.*
- *To write a sequence of poems linked by theme or form.*

Activity Sheet/Expectations

The American poet, Wallace Stevens (1879–1955), worked alone and did not belong to any literary group or school. Perhaps, in consequence, his work has an original style. 'Thirteen Ways of Looking at a Blackbird' is a series of images. The first part of the poem (1) is often reproduced on its own in anthologies, either as a single image or with Japanese haiku poetry, which is also concerned with creating vivid images.

The children are asked to consider the various ways in which each part is linked. For example, there are connections, not only through the blackbird itself but also through:
- the rhythm and movement of the bird (*moving, whirled, whistling, traced*);
- nature (in the depiction of landscape);
- the seasons (autumn, winter).

The children may find aspects of the poem particularly challenging, but should focus on the pictures that are conjured up in their own minds. They can use the poem as a model to write their own series of images about a creature or object. If they wish, they need only take the form of the poem, for example they could create views of a clock, listing the numbers, which could be presented as a shape poem.

Further activities

The children can examine a range of syllable poems, such as cinquain (a twenty-two syllable poem) and renga (a series of haiku), most of which are concerned with strong images. They can compare these with 'Thirteen Ways of Looking at a Blackbird.'

Note: No help is given with the meaning of difficult words in the poem, such as *euphony*, and *equipage* so the children should have dictionaries available to consult. See also 'Six Views of a Waterfall', 'Ten Things in a Wizard's Pocket' and 'Cardinal Ideograms' (see 'Resources').

Resources

AS 'A poem of images'; dictionaries; *Collected Poems for Children* by Gareth Owen in which 'Six Views of a Waterfall' can be found (Macmillan); *Read Me* compiled by Gabby Morgan in which 'Ten Things in a Wizard's Pocket' can be found (Macmillan); 'Cardinal Ideograms', see page 35 of this book

A poem of images

Name: .... **Date:** ....

1. Read the following poem by Wallace Stevens.

Thirteen Ways of Looking at a Blackbird

1 Among twenty snowy mountains,
The only moving thing
Was the eye of the blackbird.

2 I was of three minds,
like a tree
In which there are three blackbirds.

3 The blackbird whirled in the autumn winds.
It was a small part of the pantomime.

4 A man and a woman
Are one.
A man and a woman and a blackbird.
Are one.

5 I do not know which to prefer,
The beauty of inflections
Or the beauty of innuendoes,
The blackbird whistling
Or just after.

6 Icicles filled the long window
With barbaric glass.
The shadow of the blackbird
Crossed it, to and fro.
The mood
Traced in the shadow
An indecipherable cause.

7 O thin men of Haddam,
Why do you imagine golden birds?
Do you not see how the blackbird
Walks around the feet
Of the women about you?

8 I know noble accents
And lucid, inescapable rhythms;
But I know, too,
That the blackbird is involved
In what I know.

9 When the blackbird flew of sight,
It marked the edge
Of one of many circles.

10 At the sight of blackbirds
Flying in a green light,
Even the bawds of euphony
Would cry out sharply.

11 He rode over Connecticut
In a glass coach.
Once, a fear pierced him,
In that he mistook
The shadow of his equipage
For blackbirds.

12 The river is moving
The blackbird must be flying.

13 It was evening all afternoon.
It was snowing
And it was going to snow.
The blackbird sat
In the cedar limbs.

2. Each part of the poem is linked by the blackbirds. How else are they linked? Think about what the blackbirds are doing, where the poem is set and the cycles of the year.

3. Write your own poem in a similar way. It could be about a creature or an object. Imagine you are looking at it from different angles. What does it look like?

Comparing and contrasting

Learning objectives

Text level
- *To look at connections and contrasts in the work of different writers.*
- *To comment critically on the overall impact of a poem, showing how language and themes have been developed.*

Activity Sheet/Expectations

In this activity, both poems are concerned with the passing of time and take a despairing view of age. The modes of expression and patterning are different, however. The first uses repetition and has an insistent rhythm and rhyme that emphasises the subject. The second, 'The Seven Ages of Man', written in blank verse, is slower-paced with a more subtle patterning. The latter, spoken by Jacques in *As You Like It*, crystallises the common human experience. Both poems are profound and have achieved posterity in their own ways.

Some of the above points will not be immediately obvious to the children, but the questions on the activity sheet encourage them to explore both poems in some depth. They should consider their responses to the poems initially, note similarities and differences covering the areas on the activity sheet (and discussed above) and use this work to write a critical commentary. Some help is given here and you may wish the children to incorporate quotations from the poems to support what they write (see below). Some help is also given with the language but the children should use the context to help them decipher unfamiliar words, and in the case of *sans* any knowledge they have of French.

Further activities

Show the children how they can support critical commentaries by incorporating short quotations into their sentences, for example *Shakespeare sees human life as acted out on 'a stage' in which we play 'many parts'*, from birth to death.

You may wish to discuss blank verse with some of the children. It is a controlled verse form written in iambic pentameter (a ten-syllable line with five stresses) without obvious rhyme, but with subtle patterning.

Some children may wish to write two contrasting poems on the subjects of youth and age. They could use the same rhyme scheme for both, perhaps taking a cue from 'Lines on a Clock in Chester Cathedral' or write in free verse. They could also write from the perspectives of different characters. Alternatively, they could write an optimistic poem about age, perhaps using a relative as their subject. For further classic and traditional poems on time, youth and age, you might look at 'Loveliest of Trees the Cherry Now' by A E Houseman and 'Sevens' by Eleanor Farjeon (see 'Resources').

Resources

AS 'Comparing two poems'; *A Puffin Book of Verse* edited by Eleanor Graham and in which both 'Loveliest of Trees the Cherry Now' by A E Houseman and 'Sevens' by Eleanor Farjeon can be found

Comparing two poems

Name: .... **Date:** ....

1. Read these two poems on age.

Lines on a Clock in Chester Cathedral

When as a child, I laughed and wept,
    Time crept.
When as a youth, I dreamt and talked,
    Time walked.
When I became a full-grown man,
    Time ran.
When older still I daily grew,
    Time flew.
Soon I shall find on travelling on –
    Time gone.
O Christ, wilt Thou have saved me then?
    Amen.

Henry Twells

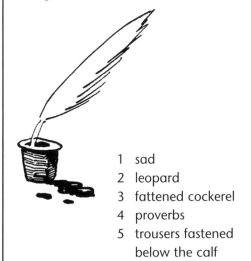

1 sad
2 leopard
3 fattened cockerel
4 proverbs
5 trousers fastened
    below the calf

The Seven Ages of Man

All the world's a stage,
And all the men and women merely players:
They have their exits and their entrances;
And one man in his time plays many parts,
His acts being seven ages. At first the infant,
Mewling and puking in the nurse's arms.
And then the whining school-boy, with his satchel
And shining morning face, creeping like snail
Unwillingly to school. And then the lover,
Sighing like furnace, with a woeful[1] ballad
Made to his mistress' eyebrow. Then a soldier,
Full of strange oaths, and bearded like the pard[2],
Jealous in honour, sudden and quick in quarrel,
Seeking the bubble reputation
Even in the cannon's mouth. And then the justice,
In fair round belly with good capon[3] lin'd,
With eyes severe, and beard of formal cut,
Full of wise saws[4] and modern instances;
And so he plays his part. The sixth age shifts
Into the lean and slipper'd pantaloon[5],
With spectacles on nose and pouch on side,
His youthful hose, well sav'd, a world too wide
For his shrunk shank; and his big manly voice,
Turning again towards childish treble, pipes
And whistles in his sound. Last scene of all,
That ends this strange eventful history,
In second childishness and mere oblivion,
Sans teeth, sans eyes, sans taste, sans everything.

From As You Like It Act II Scene VII, *by William Shakespeare (1564–1616)*

2. How do these poems make you feel? Do you agree with their points of view?

3. Draw up a table to compare the similarities and differences between them. Think about the titles, the themes, any rhyme and rhythm and how all these relate to meaning.

4. Write a commentary on both poems, comparing them. Organise your work into paragraphs and use linking phrases, such as *In the first poem, the theme is of ...,* *The poet says ...*

Reviews

Learning objectives

Text level
- *To write a brief helpful review tailored for real audiences.*
- *To compare texts in writing, drawing out: their different styles and preoccupations; their strengths and weaknesses; their different values and appeal to a reader.*

Activity Sheet/Expectations

Here the children are asked to read and study a book review. It is assumed they will already have had some experience of writing reviews since this example introduces the children to critical commentary, while still maintaining a style suitable to its target audience. The children should read the annotations and add their own, noting that the review:

- is written in the present tense;
- addresses the reader directly in the second person (you);
- has an informal tone;
- uses terminology and literary phrases (*themes, drawn in greater depth*).

The children can then make notes about a book of their choice using what they have learned.

Further activities

The children should use their notes to write their own review. It could be about a recent novel or story they have read but it should be addressed to other children and be written in a suitable style. They can use the review of *Multiply by two* as a model, and cover character, plot, theme, style and critical judgements. In particular, they should be careful to outline the plot briefly.

The children could also write a review of a non-fiction book. This will allow them to make comparisons between fiction and non-fiction texts. When reviewing the latter they can consider:

- clarity – are explanations, clear?
- presentation – do illustrations serve a useful purpose? Would they appeal to the reader?
- organisation – is there an index, glossary and contents page to help the reader?
- opinions expressed – does the author express an opinion about the topic being covered?

Note: The children should seek out several non-fiction books to study before selecting one. It is best if they focus on books targeted at a particular age range.

Resources

AS 'A book review'; fiction and non-fiction books

A book review

Name: .... **Date:** ....

1. Read this book review and the notes around it.

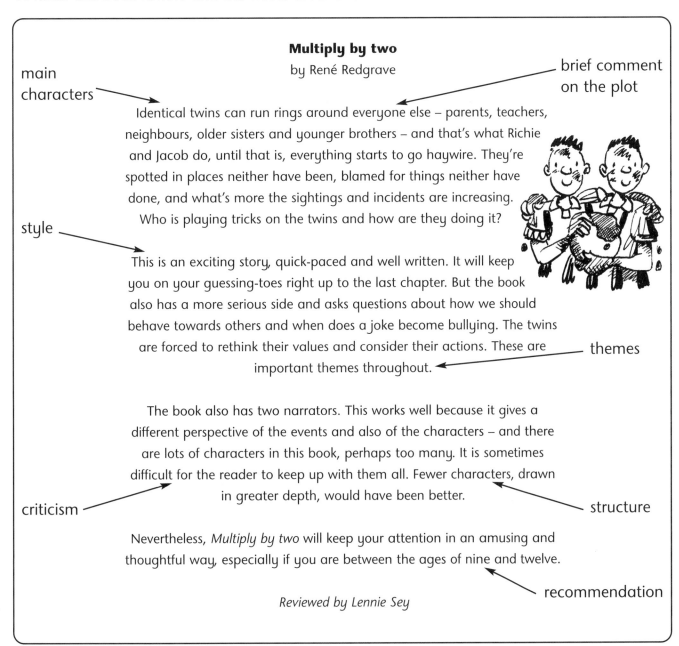

main characters

brief comment on the plot

Multiply by two
by René Redgrave

Identical twins can run rings around everyone else – parents, teachers, neighbours, older sisters and younger brothers – and that's what Richie and Jacob do, until that is, everything starts to go haywire. They're spotted in places neither have been, blamed for things neither have done, and what's more the sightings and incidents are increasing. Who is playing tricks on the twins and how are they doing it?

style

This is an exciting story, quick-paced and well written. It will keep you on your guessing-toes right up to the last chapter. But the book also has a more serious side and asks questions about how we should behave towards others and when does a joke become bullying. The twins are forced to rethink their values and consider their actions. These are important themes throughout.

themes

The book also has two narrators. This works well because it gives a different perspective of the events and also of the characters – and there are lots of characters in this book, perhaps too many. It is sometimes difficult for the reader to keep up with them all. Fewer characters, drawn in greater depth, would have been better.

criticism

structure

Nevertheless, *Multiply by two* will keep your attention in an amusing and thoughtful way, especially if you are between the ages of nine and twelve.

Reviewed by Lennie Sey

recommendation

2. Now add notes of your own. Think about these questions:
● In what tense is the review written?
● How is the reader addressed? What word tells you?
● In what tone is the review written? Formal or informal? How can you tell?
● What terminology tells you that it is a book review? (Underline some words.)

3. Now use the review as a model to make notes about a book you have read. This will help you to write your own review.

Skimming and scanning

Learning objectives

Text level
- *To appraise a text quickly and effectively; to retrieve information from it.*
- *To secure the skills of skimming, scanning and efficient reading so that research is fast and effective.*

Activity Sheet/Expectations

Here the children are asked to skim through two sixteenth-century recipes to try and understand the gist of them. They are then asked to write both recipes in modern English, which will need more careful study. The second recipe is more difficult than the first and requires some reorganisation. It would be useful if the translations were read to a partner afterwards to test clarity. The following are modern versions of both recipes.

Eggs in Mustard Sauce
Boiled eggs: Boil your eggs until almost hard, then peel them and cut them into quarters. Melt little butter in a frying pan until brown. Add a little vinegar, mustard, pepper and salt. Pour over the eggs and serve.

Cheese Tart
To make a cheese tart: Take fine pastry and roll it out as thin as you can. Grate the cheese and pound it in a mortar with egg yolks. Add some clarified butter. Put the mixture into a good quality dish lined with the pastry. Cover with pastry and seal. Bake it and, when done, serve.

Further activities

The texts can be studied further, with the children scanning both texts to compare them. In particular they could note the inconsistent spelling (*Eggs – Egs*), that capitals are used for most ingredients and at the beginning of the recipes, commas are more frequently used and full stops less so.

Ask the children to try writing a simple recipe using archaic language, for example how to fry an egg or make porridge. They may need to use an etymological dictionary, although they should use the context first to guess the meaning of words. The *New Oxford Dictionary of English* also contains many archaic words, including *seethe*, of which *sodde/sodden* is the past participle. The children could also use ICT.

You might also like to look at *Food and Cooking in 16th Century Britain: History and Recipes* (see 'Resources').

Resources

AS 'Egges in Mustarde or Tarte of Cheese?'; etymological dictionary; computer for ICT work; *Food and Cooking in 16th Century Britain: History and Recipes* by Peter Brears (English Heritage)

Egges in Mustarde or Tarte of Cheese?

Name: .... **Date:** ....

1. These recipes were written in the sixteenth century. Skim them quickly, and try to guess the meaning of the words as you go. Remember, the preparation is not so very different from modern methods.

Egges in Mustarde

Sodde Egges: Seeth your Egges almost harde, then peele them and cut them in quarters, then take a little Butter in a frying panne and melt it a little broune, then put it in to the panne, a little Vinegar, Mustarde, Pepper and Salte, and then put it into a platter upon your Egges.

From *The Widow's Treasure* by J Partridge

Tarte of Cheese

To make a Tarte of Cheese: Take good fine paste and drive it as thin as you can. Then take cheese, pare it, mince it, and bray it in a morter with the yolks of Egs til it be like paste, then put it in a faire dish with clarified butter and then put it abroad into your paste and cover it with a faire cut cover, and so bake it; that doon, serve it forth.

From *A Book of Cookrye very necessary for all such as delight therein by Edward Allde*

2. Now write out each recipe in modern English. You can change the punctuation and, where necessary, the order of the words, so the recipes are clear, but as far as possible keep to the originals.

Selecting the style

Learning objectives

Text level
- *To select the appropriate style and form to suit a specific purpose and audience, drawing on knowledge of different non-fiction text types.*
- To write a leaving speech.

Activity Sheet/Expectations

The children are presented with a scenario in which they must write a speech for a friend who is leaving school. Several features need to be taken into account and the children should try to adopt a formal style that is tempered by the shared experiences of the speaker and the audience. The children will need to use their imaginations when considering content and should choose suitable expressions.

The children will also need to use appropriate connectives to sequence the events, working from Kitty's early school days, to the present time and beyond to the future. Though the present tense will be the main one used, the past and future will also need to be used. Help is given on the activity sheet, where the children are given a series of features from which to choose. They should circle first, second and third person, present, past and future tense, conditionals, paragraphs, introduction, conclusion and formal style. Some children may be able to add other features to the list. Notes can be made on separate pieces of paper.

Further activities

The children could carry out a role-play exercise in suitable pairs and deliver their speeches to each other. They can analyse the strengths and weaknesses together and make modifications in the light of agreements.

This activity can be extended to develop interviewing skills. These may range from using interview techniques when conducting questionnaires to carrying out historical investigations (such as interviewing grandparents). The skills needed by the interviewee can also be developed, for example role-play involving an interview for a place at a new school can be a particularly useful exercise. The children could use index cards as prompts when delivering their speeches. They would need to note the main points on a series of cards.

Resources

AS 'Helping Kitty'; blank note cards

Helping Kitty

Name: .... **Date:** ....

Your friend Kitty is leaving school because her family are moving to another town. Kitty has been at the school since she was an infant and knows all the children and teachers extremely well. She is very sad about leaving and would like to write a memorable speech as a way of saying goodbye to everybody. She also thinks that the speech will stop her becoming too upset on the day she leaves, because it will focus her mind. However, she is not sure what to say or how to say it.

1. Circle all the features that you think will apply to the speech. Remember, it may be written in more than one person and tense.

first person	second person	third person
present tense	past tense	future tense
conditionals (*would, should, if*)		slang
paragraphs	introduction	conclusion
formal style	informal style	diagrams
as an argument	as a report	as a letter

2. Make notes on the content.
- What kinds of things should Kitty say?
- Who will she thank?
- Will she mention funny incidents that have happened?
- Will she mention where she is going?
- Will she talk about her future?

3. Make notes on how Kitty will deliver her speech. What kind of expressions will she use? Add your own to the following:

I would like to say   I hope to   I am sad   I remember

4. Now write Kitty's speech for her!

Objectives grid

	Word	page	sentence	page	text	page
T1	Spelling strategies	4	Forming complex sentences	8	Commenting on non-fiction language	4
			Understanding the semicolon	8	Writing a leaflet	4
	Change of words over time	6			Recognising the work of established authors	8
					Responding to literature	10
					Manipulating narrative perspective	10, 12, 14
					Planning own narrative writing	14
					Writing a playscript	16
					Writing poems, including active verbs and personification	18
					Distinguishing between implicit and explicit points of view in autobiography	20
					Developing a journalistic style	22
					Writing an editorial	22
T2	Inventing and using mnemonics	24	Investigating active and passive verbs	28	Understanding narrative structure	32
	Proverbs	26	Investigating conditionals	30	Writing own story	32
			Investigating past and future conditionals	30	Investigating poets playing with meanings	34
					Identifying key features in literature	36
					Understanding parody	38
					Using parody	38
					Using parody constructing arguments	40
					Writing a balanced report	42
T3	Practising and extending vocabulary	44, 46	Revising language conventions and grammatical features	50	Annotating passages	52
					Discussing and writing a sequence of linked poems	54
	Experimenting with language	48	Conducting language investigations	52	Looking at connections and contrasts in writers' work	56
					Commenting critically on a poem	56
					Writing a brief helpful review	59
					Comparing texts in writing	58
					Appraising a text and retrieving information	60
					Skimming and scanning	60
					Selecting appropriate style when writing non-fiction	62
					Writing a speech	62